That's _Doctor_ Sinatra, You Little Bimbo!

Doonesbury books by G. B. Trudeau

Still a Few Bugs in the System
The President Is a Lot Smarter Than You Think
But This War Had Such Promise
Call Me When You Find America
Guilty, Guilty, Guilty!
"What Do We Have for the Witnesses, Johnnie?"
Dare To Be Great, Ms. Caucus
Wouldn't a Gremlin Have Been More Sensible?
"Speaking of Inalienable Rights, Amy . . ."
You're Never Too Old for Nuts and Berries
An Especially Tricky People
As the Kid Goes for Broke
Stalking the Perfect Tan
"Any Grooming Hints for Your Fans, Rollie?"
But the Pension Fund Was Just Sitting There
We're Not Out of the Woods Yet
A Tad Overweight, but Violet Eyes to Die For
And That's My Final Offer!
He's Never Heard of You, Either
In Search of Reagan's Brain
Ask for May, Settle for June
Unfortunately, She Was Also Wired for Sound
The Wreck of the "Rusty Nail"
You Give Great Meeting, Sid
Doonesbury: A Musical Comedy
Check Your Egos at the Door

In Large Format
The Doonesbury Chronicles
Doonesbury's Greatest Hits
The People's Doonesbury
Doonesbury Dossier: The Reagan Years

a Doonesbury book by

GB Trudeau.

That's _Doctor_ Sinatra, You Little Bimbo!

An Owl Book / Henry Holt and Company / New York

Published by Henry Holt and Company,
521 Fifth Avenue, New York, New York 10175.

Published simultaneously in Canada.

Library of Congress Catalog Card Number: 85-82193

ISBN: 0-03-008537-3

First Edition

Printed in the United States of America

The cartoons in this book have appeared in newspapers
in the United States and abroad under the auspices of
Universal Press Syndicate.

1 3 5 7 9 10 8 6 4 2

ISBN 0-03-008537-3

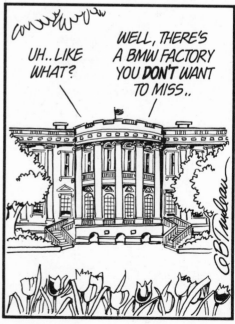

MOMENTS BEFORE AIR FORCE ONE LEFT, WHITE HOUSE IMAGE-MAKER MIKE DEAVER RELEASED THE NINTH AND FINAL VERSION OF MR. REAGAN'S SCHEDULE IN GERMANY.

SAID DEAVER IN A PREPARED STATEMENT, "BY HAVING THE PRESIDENT HONOR NAZI STORMTROOPERS AS WELL AS THEIR VICTIMS, WE FEEL WE HAVE PUT TOGETHER A BALANCED PACKAGE OF SYMBOLS."

HIS FINAL ASSIGNMENT BEHIND HIM, DEAVER IS NOW EXPECTED TO TURN HIS ATTENTION TO SOLICITING BUSINESS FOR HIS NEW P.R. FIRM.

HI. THIS IS MIKE "BITBURG" DEAVER..

=CLICK!=

SURE BEEN BURNING UP THE WIRES, BABE. I

SORRY, RICK. I'VE BEEN TRYING TO GET PEOPLE TO COME OUT FOR THE LOCAL "SILENT SCREAM" PROTEST.

"SILENT SCREAM"? BOY, YOU SURE YOU WANT TO GET INVOLVED WITH THAT?

RICK, IT'S AN IN-CENDIARY PIECE OF PROPAGANDA. THERE MAY BE A CASE TO MAKE FOR RIGHT-TO-LIFE, BUT THAT FILM ISN'T IT.

IT'S A DISGRACE THAT THE PRESIDENT WOULD ENDORSE A DOCUMENTARY THAT DISHONEST. AND NOW THERE'S EVEN TALK OF A FOLLOW-UP.

WELCOME TO "SILENT SCREAM II: THE PREQUEL."

GBTrudeau

GOOD EVENING, AND WELCOME TO "SILENT SCREAM II: THE PREQUEL."

IN "SILENT SCREAM I", WE SHOWED YOU THE TERMINATION OF A 12-WEEK-OLD PREGNANCY. TONIGHT, WE'LL BE WITNESSING THE END OF A 12-**MINUTE**-OLD PREGNANCY.

THROUGH THE MAGIC OF FIBER-OPTICS, WE'VE BEEN ABLE TO TAKE A COMPUTER-ENHANCED PHOTO OF THE CHILD IN REPOSE. AS YET, HE IS UN-AWARE OF THE DANGER HE FACES.

LET'S CALL HIM "TIMMY".

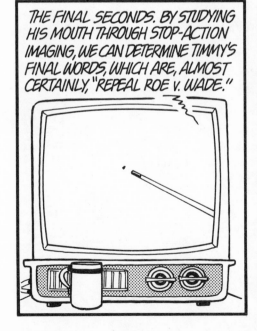

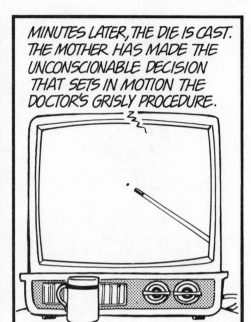

"HIS LOVE OF COUNTRY, HIS GENEROSITY FOR THOSE LESS FORTUNATE, HIS DISTINCTIVE ART..

.. AND HIS WINNING AND COMPASSIONATE PERSONA MAKE HIM ONE OF OUR MOST REMARKABLE AND DISTINGUISHED AMERICANS..

.. AND ONE WHO TRULY DID IT HIS WAY."
– Ronald Reagan
May 23, 1985

GB Trudeau

MEDAL OF FREEDOM RECIPIENT FRANK SINATRA DOING IT HIS WAY WITH TOMMY "FATSO" MARSON, DON CARLO GAMBINO, RICHARD "NERVES" FUSCO, JIMMY "THE WEASEL" FRATIANNO, JOSEPH GAMBINO AND GREG DEPALMA.

"HE HAS CARRIED ON HIS CRAFT WITH DISTINCTION AND HIGH PROFESSIONALISM..

HE HAS APPLIED HIS TALENTS TO THE BENEFIT OF MANKIND..

..AND TO THE UPLIFTING OF THE HUMAN SPIRIT."
— Citation for honorary degree, Stevens Institute, May 23, 1985

DR. FRANCIS SINATRA UPLIFTING THE SPIRITS OF ALLEGED HUMAN ANIELLO DELLACROCE, LATER CHARGED WITH THE MURDER OF GAMBINO FAMILY MEMBER CHARLEY CALISE.

ON BUDGET? ARE YOU KIDDING, CASSIE? THIS SHOOT IS THE BARGAIN OF THE YEAR!

EVERY SHOT'S BEEN ONE TAKE. IT TURNS OUT ZONKER IS A COMPLETE NATURAL IN FRONT OF THE CAMERA.

WE JUST BLOCKED THE LAST SHOT, AND LET ME TELL YOU, THERE WASN'T A DRY EYE ON THE SET.

GBTrudeau

AND I THOUGHT MR. SUN WAS OUR FRIEND, ZONKER.

HE IS, TOMMY. BUT WE HAVE TO RESPECT HIS POWER!

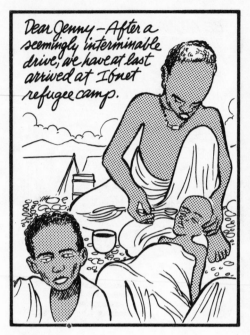

Dear Jenny—After a seemingly interminable drive, we have at last arrived at Ifnet refugee camp.

In trying to come to terms with the suffering here, one has to suspend all previous reference points. No words are adequate to describe this calamity.

The people here have as little comprehension of us as we do of them. Our worlds are totally alien to each other, except, of course, in one notable way..

HE WANTS TO KNOW WHY YOU MOVED FROM REGGAE TO TECHNO-POP.

EXPLAIN TO HIM I NEEDED TO GROW MUSICALLY.

©B Trudeau

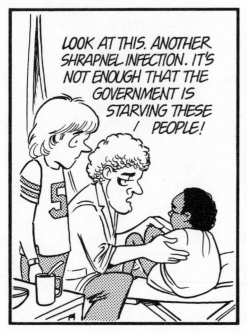

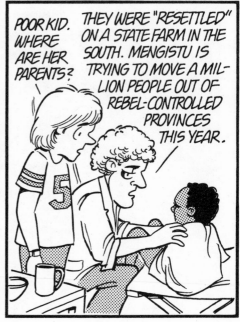

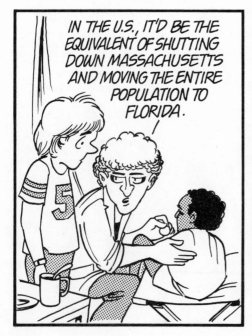

FRIENDS, CO-WORKERS, AND EX-LOVERS: WE ARE HERE TODAY TO CELEBRATE THE END OF ONE OF THE MOST EXTENSIVE MANHUNTS IN THE HISTORY OF MANHATTAN.

TONIGHT IS AN OCCASION FOR NEW BEGINNINGS. AT THE STROKE OF MIDNIGHT, I WILL BE TAKING A SOLEMN VOW TO GET ON WITH MY LIFE!

IMMEDIATELY THEREAFTER, I WILL DECLARE AN OPEN BAR, PUT ON MY SHIRELLES TAPE, KICK OFF MY SHOES AND BOP 'TIL I DROP!

AT DAWN, I LEAVE FOR TIBET.

IN YOUR UNDER-WEAR?

GBTrudeau

"WE ARE GATHERED HERE TO WITNESS THE END OF MS. MARCIA FEINBLOOM'S ACTIVE SEARCH FOR A LIFELONG COMPANION."

"WHILE RULING NOTHING OUT DEFINITIVELY, TODAY SHE CELEBRATES HER RELEASE FROM THE TYRANNY OF INFLATED EXPECTATIONS."

"SHOULD ANY PERSON HAVE REASON WHY THIS CEREMONY SHOULD NOT TAKE PLACE, SPEAK NOW OR FOREVER HOLD YOUR PEACE."

WAIT!

OH, THANK GOD! SOMEBODY GRAB HIM! WHO IS IT?

GBTrudeau